THE BOY WHO CHANGED HIS WORLD

Robert Whanslaw

Little Acorn Publishing

ACKNOWLEDGMENTS

Special thanks to my wife Sahana, for always supporting me in all my endeavors and to the world of Lean Six Sigma for accepting and enabling me to perform at a global scale.

ABOUT THE AUTHOR

Sumeet Savant is a Lean Six Sigma Master Black Belt Mentor and coach, with more than a decade of experience in executing, leading and mentoring Lean Six Sigma process improvement projects. He is a BTech, MBA, and Prince certified Practitioner. He has facilitated hundreds of process improvement projects, and coached hundreds of professionals, Yellow, Green, and Black Belts over the years. He lives in Mumbai, India with his family.

LEAN

LEAN, VALUE, AND WASTE

Lean is now a common term, synonymous with process improvement, waste elimination and cost reduction.

You probably might have heard about Lean, or might have some basic idea about Lean, or might be even working on and practicing Lean methodologies

Before we start, let us understand what the term Lean really means.

Formally defined, "**Lean** is a continuous improvement strategy, focused on **maximizing customer value**, by **minimizing waste** in all the business processes, or products."

So, now the question arises, what do the terms Value and Waste mean.

"**Value**, means something, that the customer is willing to pay for, extending this definition, we can say it is something which the customer **needs, and hence expects**, from the product or service, for which he buys it.".

And, by "**Waste** we mean, any activity or feature that **does not add value** to the product or service, from the point of view of the customer."

The Japanese term for Waste so defined, is **Muda**.

Some of the examples of Waste or Muda are,

• Unnecessary travel like driving, or riding.

• Waiting for approval.

• Unnecessary Movement like bending, or stretching.

• Producing more than required.

Though Lean is primarily focused on reduction of waste, the Lean strategies framework is much broader.

To understand the Lean framework, it is a must to be well acquainted with something that is known as the **House of Lean**.

.

HOUSE OF LEAN

The collection of Lean concepts, practices, and tools, put together in a container that looks like a home, to act as a framework for implementing a complete Lean system is known as the **House of Lean.**

House of Lean: Goals

The first component of House of Lean is its roof, which represents the **Goals** of the business.

Most businesses have similar goals as follows,

• Highest Quality

Quality in terms of features and characteristics of the products or services provided to the customer.

• Lowest Cost

Lowest cost in terms of raw materials, man power, and machinery required to design, develop and deliver the products.

• **Shortest Lead Time**

Shortest time taken from initiation of idea to going to market of the products or services.

The roof of the House of quality is depicted in the following figure.

House of Lean: JIT

The next component of the House of Lean is its left pillar, which represents the **JIT or Just In Time** concepts, practices, and tools.

Just In Time

JIT is a methodology aimed primarily at reducing flow times within production system as well as response times from suppliers and to customers. It aims at reducing the inventory, and overproduction by producing just in time to meet the customer demands.

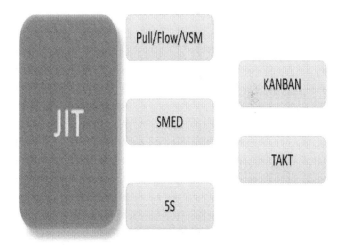

The JIT concepts, practices, and tools include the following,

• **Pull**

Pull means producing to the customer demand.

• **Flow**

In Lean, the process flow, which means to move along in a steady, continuous stream, should be free of waste, and issues, to ensure a steady continuous uninterrupted flow.

• **VSM**

Value Stream Mapping is a technique to chart the flow of the processes, identify wastes in the flow, establishing root causes for the wastes, and identifying ways to reduce or eliminate the wastes.

• **KANBAN**

Kanban is a scheduling system for lean manufacturing and just-in-time manufacturing, that makes use of cards to track, schedule and control production.

• **SMED**

Single-minute exchange of die, is a lean production method to provide a rapid and efficient way of converting a manufacturing process from running the current product to running the next product, it is a system for reducing the time taken for equipment changeovers.

• **TAKT**

TAKT Time, is the average time or rate at which a product needs to be completed in order to meet customer demand.

• 5S

5S is a workplace organization framework that uses five Japanese words to represent its principles or phases: Seiri(Sort), Seiton(Set in order), Seiso(Shine), Seiketsu(Standardize), and Shitsuke(Sustain).

House of Lean: JIDOKA

The next component of the House of Lean is its right pillar, which represents the **JIDOKA** concepts, practices, and tools.

JIDOKA

JIDOKA, also known as Autonomation which means "Intelligent Automation" or "Humanized Automation", is an automation which implements some sort of monitory techniques, making it "aware" enough to detect an abnormal situation, and stop the machine, to enable the workers to stop the production line, investigate the root causes and fix the issue.

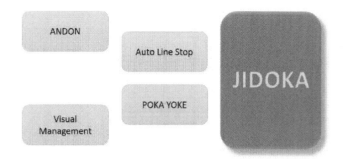

The JIDOKA concepts, practices, and tools include the following,

• ANDON

ANDON is an alerting system that notifies management, maintenance, and other workers of a quality or process problem. It can be manual or automated.

• Auto Line Stop

Auto Line Stop is a system that stops the production process whenever an issue or defect occurs, it can be automated or manual.

• POKA YOKE

POKA YOKE or Mistake Proofing, is a lean mechanism that helps an equipment operator avoid (yokeru) mistakes (poka). It eliminates product defects by preventing, correcting, or drawing attention to human errors as they occur.

• Visual Management

Visual Management is a lean system to manage production and processes through visual signs and controls.

House of Lean: Standardization and Stability

The next component of the House of Lean is its strong base, which represents the **Standardization and Stability** concepts, practices, and tools.

Standardization and Stability

Standardization and Stability, deal with standardizing the work, processes, and workplace, with an aim to consistently achieve the best, and with stabilizing the processes to avoid fluctuations and variations in output.

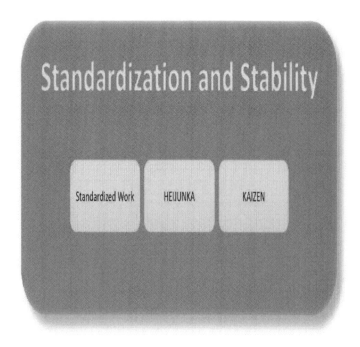

The Standardization and Stability concepts, practices, and tools include the following,

• Standardized Work

Standardized Work is a work derived from best practices and lessons learned while performing the work, to do it in a most efficient way, to improve productivity and avoid rework.

• HEIJUNKA

HEIJUNKA or leveling, is a technique to level the work or production load to reduce unevenness or Mura.

• KAIZEN

KAIZEN is a continuous improvement approach based on the idea that small, continuous or consistent positive changes can reap major improvements.

House of Lean: Respect for Individual

The final and core component of the House of Lean is to establish the values of **Respect for Individual**.

Respect for Individual

Respect for Individual, deals with empowering, motivating, and supporting the workforce to effectively and consistently participate in lean methodologies to guarantee and sustain improvements.

The Respect for Individual concepts, practices, and tools include the following,

• Empowerment, Motivation, and Support

Empowerment, Motivation, and Support is a management philosophy and ideology to empower, motivate, and support the workforce to encourage them identify the areas for improvement, and participate consistently and willingly without the need to be told to do so.

• Gemba Kaizen Circles

Gemba Kaizen is a Japanese concept of continuous improvement designed for enhancing processes and reducing waste at the workplace including the workforce, or the people that work at the location. Gemba refers to the location where value is created, while Kaizen relates to improvements.

• HOSHIN Planning

HOSHIN Planning is a strategic planning process in which strategic goals are communicated throughout the company and then put into action.

House of Lean

With all the components combined, the House of Lean looks similar to the following depicted figure.

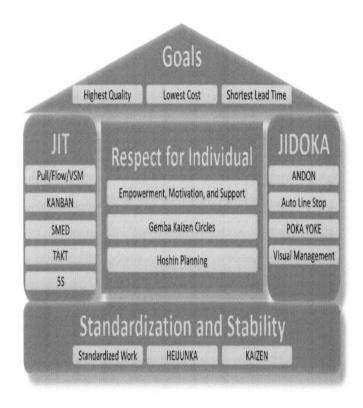

FIVE PRINCIPLES OF LEAN

There are five principles of lean, based around customer, values, quality and wastes. They are,

Define Value

To be able to understand the first principle of Lean, it is essential to know what "Value" and "Quality" are.

Value is something that the customer is willing to pay for. It is something that the customer expects from the product or service, he buys. It is something, which satisfies the customer's needs.

Quality of a product or service is the degree of value the product or service adds to the customer. It means, the degree to which the product or service satisfies the customer's needs

For a company to survive and succeed, it is essential that it understands the needs of its customers, and how its products and services can satisfy its customer's needs by providing the right quality and adding the right value.

So, it is very essential to identify and define value from the point of view of the customer, and produce products and services that deliver maximum quality, and value.

Due to this reason, the very first principle in lean states to define or identify value from the point of view of the customer.

What is valuable to customer, or what are the customer's needs can be found out by collecting the VOC or the **Voice of customer**.

There are many ways VOC can be gathered, such as interviews, surveys, and market and web analytics that can help you discover what customers seek value in.

Map Value Stream

Once you identify what the customer values in your products or services, the next step is to understand the steps and activities involved in creating the value.

The **Value stream** is the complete end to end flow of a product's life-cycle.

It starts from the getting the raw materials used to make the product, and goes on up to the customer's buying, using, and ultimately disposing of the product.

Mapping the Value Stream, in this context, is an exercise to create a flowchart or a process map of all the activities involved in the product's complete life cycle.

The **Value stream process map** thus created outlines each and every step of the process for each part of the business, right from market research, to R&D, to Design, to Development, to Production, to Marketing, to Sales and Services, etc.

Only by thoroughly studying and understanding the value stream can a company understand the wastes associated, and hence find opportunities to reduce costs and tackle issues, in manufacturing and delivery of a product or service.

Supplier and customer partnership is one of the core ideas of Lean as it helps understand the complete supply chain, and eliminate wastes and other issues from the entire value stream.

Create Flow

Once you have the Value Stream Map ready, the next step will be to create Flow.

To **Create Flow**, means to ensure that the flow of the process steps is smooth and free of interruptions or delays.

The first action to achieve this is to analyze the process map for wastes.

Once the wastes are analyzed, you can perform root cause analysis to understand the causes behind the wastes.

These causes needs to be acted upon to ensure the flow of steps and activities are smoothed and made free of any issues, problems, or bottlenecks.

Once the wastes are eliminated, you can find further ways to maximize efficiencies.

Some strategies for ensuring smooth flow include breaking down steps, re-engineering the steps, work and production leveling, creating cross-functional and multi-skilled departments, suppliers, and workforce.

Establish Pull

Once you have eliminated the wastes in the process, and created the flow, the next step would be to establish Pull.

Pull is producing as per customer demand.

Inventory and Overproduction are two of the most problematic wastes in any production systems.

The ultimate goal of the pull system is to limit stocking up the inventory, and to produce only to meet the customer demand

To achieve this, you need to effectively look at the operations of the business in reverse on the value stream maps.

The idea is to capture and analyze the exact moments as to when the customers actually need the product.

This helps to implement the JIT mode of manufacturing and operations where products are produced just in time when the customers need them.

Extending this further, this also helps to get and procure even the raw materials, just in time when the production needs them.

Pursue Perfection

Once you have eliminated the wastes in the process, created the flow, and established the Pull, the final step is to keep the improvements sustained, and ongoing.

Perfection is to achieve the absolute best in anything that the company does.

So, it is absolutely not enough to just eliminate wastes, create flow, and establish pull.

You need to develop a mindset of continual improvement.

Each and every employee should strive towards perfection, and work with an aim to deliver consistent value.

This relentless pursuit of perfection is key attitude of an organization that is "going for lean", and makes Lean thinking and continuous process improvement a part of the organizational culture.

The following figure depicts the five principles of Lean.

WASTES

TYPES OF WORK

Before we can understand what waste is, it is very important to understand what are the types of work.

There are three types of work based on the customer's point of view, as to how the customer looks at the work done.

They are,

• **Value Added Work**

• **Business Necessary Work**

• **Non Value Added Work**

Now, we will see each of these work types in detail.

Value Added Work

Value Added Work is the first type of work activity.

It is type of activity or work, for which the customer is willing to pay for.

Any activity which the customer perceives as actually adding value to the product or service is termed as **Value Added Work**.

These activities have the following characteristics which classify these activities as value adding.

• Change/Transformation

These activities change or transform an item from one condition to another, or from one state to another, with an overall focus of reaching the final state of the product or service, which the customer needs.

• First Time Right

These activities are done in a right way, or correctly the very first time, that is without the need for corrections or rework.

• Customer is willing to pay

These activities are activities which the customer wants done, as he perceives them to be necessary steps to create the product or service he expects, and hence is willing to pay for.

Business Necessary Work

Business Necessary Work is the second type of work activity.

It is type of activity or work, for which though the customer is unwilling to pay, still needs to be performed to create the product or services the customer needs.

This type of activity may have similar characteristics as Value Adding Activity like, transformation of an item from one state to another, or done correctly the first time.

However, the important difference which classify this type of activity differently is that the customer does not care for this activity, and hence is unwilling to pay.

Such work includes any work that might be performed to protect the business, or to comply with established policies or standards, or even as precautionary measures.

This type of work is also known as the following,

• **Business Value Added Work.**

• **Value Enabling Work.**

• **Necessary Non Value Added Work.**

Non Value Added Work

Non Value Added Work is the third type of work activity.

This work activity adds absolutely no value to the product or service.

This work activity neither transforms nor helps in achieving the end product or service.

And most importantly, the customer is not willing to pay for this work activity.

This work activity is referred to as waste, or the **Muda** in Japanese.

To figure out any non value activity in your products or service, it is best to look at them from the point of view of customer, and think whether the customer would be willing to pay for the activity.

Lean focuses on eliminating waste, by reducing or removing the non value activities from the value stream.

Example

Imagine you need to travel from one city to another, on a road.

Traveling on the road represents the value flow, as it helps you reach your destination.

Value added work would be you driving a vehicle on that road to reach your destination.

Non Value added work would be any additional turns, stops, and interruptions you may have to take while driving due to various reasons like traffic, broken pathways, pedestrians crossing roads etc.

Business Value added work would be any additional turns, stops interruptions you may have to take while driving due to the road and traffic rules like the zebra crossing, traffic lights, etc.

NEED TO REMOVE WASTES

Before we proceed any further, let us quickly look at a visual representation that will help you understand how important it is to remove waste from our services and products.

Consider a process, a typical process will have certain value added activities, and certain non value added activities.

Following is a depiction of a value stream of such a typical process.

Value added work is depicted in green, and non value added work in red.

This may appear quite normal, and acceptable, however just wait and watch, what happens when we analyze it.

Looking at the value stream map, we may think that it depicted a normal acceptable waste presence.

However, let us now split, and separate the value added work from the non value added work.

Now look at the newly arranged value stream map, depicted in the following figure.

You will get to clearly see what the wastes are doing to our processes.

As you can see, the minor wastes hidden here and there when taken together do appear huge, and sometimes huge enough to harm the process.

Let us continue the analysis one more step further.

Let us now actually calculate the percentage distribution of the value added and the non value added work or activity in our process.

And then let us plot the distribution in a pie chart, to get a visual feel of the percentage distribution.

Depicted below is the figure of pie distribution so created.

If you see, the total waste in our process is 43%, with so much waste hidden in our processes no wonder they are so costly.

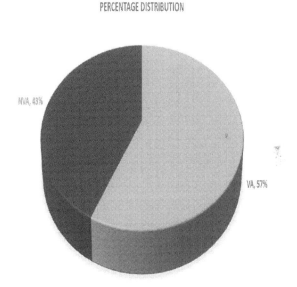

PERCENTAGE DISTRIBUTION

NVA, 43%

VA, 57%

VA NVA

Lean focuses on saving these costs, by eliminating wastes and improving processes.

Imagine that the total time taken by our process is 2000 person hours, and per hour uniform cost of 50 USD.

So, the total cost of our process then would be 100000 USD

And, since 43% of the time was going waste,

The process clearly wasted as much as 860 person hour per run, and a dollar wastage of 43000 USD

If we now consider that this process runs just even once per day, just imagine the kind of loss this process is creating annually.

The reason why Lean is so powerful is that it focuses on searching such opportunities where costs can be saved.

And, as we have seen so far, to achieve the highest cost reductions in our processes, it is imperative that we need to hunt for wastes in them.

And, to hunt for wastes, we need to have a clear understanding of what the wastes are, their types, and how we can control and eliminate them.

THE 3 M'S

Any discussion on wastes, will be incomplete if we do not talk about the 3 infamous M's in the Lean world, the Muda, Muri, and Mura.

Muda

Muda in Japanese means useless, or waste, and comes in eight forms.

The figure below clearly depicts Muda, as can be seen, the truck is not being utilized to its fullest capacity, and hence considerable space is being **wasted**.

Muri

Muri is the overloading or overburdening of employees, or machines, or processes.

Employees, machines, and even processes, have thresholds or limits, which should be respected.

Trying to get more done from them, beyond their capacity, can lead to break downs or stress, and low morale.

The figure below clearly depicts Muri, as can be seen, the truck is overloaded to the point of tipping or loosing balance.

Establishing TAKT time, standardizing work, and implementing pull systems are some of the ways to avoid Muri.

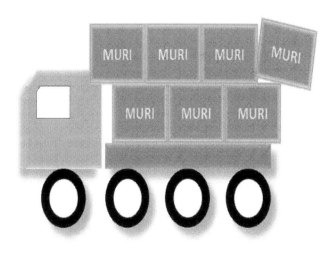

OVERLOAD

Mura

Mura is the unevenness or fluctuation or variation in the work, or workplace.

We often see this in products and services due to rushed delivery, or poor planning.

Establishing TAKT time, leveling work (Heijunka), implementing Six Sigma and pull systems are some of the ways to avoid Mura.

The figure below clearly depicts Mura, as can be seen, the two carriages of the truck are unevenly loaded.

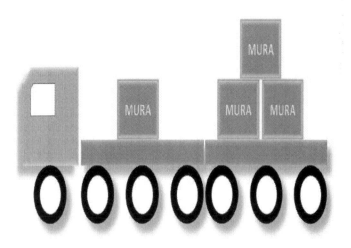

UNEVENNESS

The Ideal State

No Muda, No Muri, and No Mura is the ideal state to be achieved and sustained in any lean system.

Processes should be free or wastes, overloading, and unevenness or variation.

The figure below clearly depicts a No Muda, Muri, Mura state, as can be seen, the truck is carrying just the ideal load, free of the 3 M's.

VALUE STREAM MAPPING

VALUE STREAM

Before we proceed with the Value Stream Mapping it is essential to first understand what a Value Stream means.

Value Stream is the set of all activities, processes, and steps involved in creating and delivering value to the customer.

It starts right at the idea creation step and includes all the necessary steps including design, development, delivery and after services of the value product.

Understanding the value stream is critically important if you wish to deliver value to your customers, reduce wastes in your processes, and achieve cost effectiveness.

Lean implementation is possible only when you know your business processes and value streams.

VALUE STREAM MAPPING

Value Stream Mapping is the single most essential, yet simple tool, to effectively identify wastes in any business processes.

It is an enhanced mapping tool that maps the current and future states of processes, to help reduce wastes.

It is an integral and the most important part of a lean tool kit.

Its power lies in identifying waste, its sources, and presenting them in an easy to understand visual manner.

We can formally define the Value Stream Mapping as a

mapping tool to analyze the current processes, identify value added and non value added steps and design a future state map of the process, to achieve overall waste reduction.

VALUE STREAM MAPPING CLASSIFICATION BASED ON NATURE OF PROCESSES

Value Stream Mapping is broadly classified into two types, based on the nature of processes.

They are,

• **Production Value Stream Mapping** , also known as the Developmental Value Stream Mapping

• **Transactional Value Stream Mapping** , also known as the Operational Value Stream Mapping

Production Value Stream Mapping

Production Value Stream Mapping , is also known as the Developmental Value Stream Mapping

This type of mapping is done for value streams that include manufacturing, production, or developmental processes.

Examples of Production Value Streams can include,

• Development of new products.

• Adding new features products.

• Building up of new services.

• Modification of existing services.

• Building new systems.

• Enhancing existing systems.

Transactional Value Stream Mapping

Transactional Value Stream Mapping , is also known as the Operational Value Stream Mapping

This type of mapping is done for value streams that include business operations, and transactions with customers.

Examples of Transactional Value Streams can include,

• Buying, selling, or servicing of products.

• Getting into bonds or agreements.

• Selling, purchasing, and using of services.

• Marketing, selling, buying or maintenance of systems.

The following figure depicts the different types of Value Stream Mapping, based on the nature of the processes.

Value stream Mapping Types

Production Value Stream Mapping	Transactional Value Stream Mapping
▪ Developmental Value Stream Mapping. ▪ Development or Building of new products, services, systems. ▪ Adding new features to products, services or new systems.	▪ Operational Value Stream Mapping. ▪ Buying, selling, or maintenance of products, systems, or services.

VALUE STREAM MAPPING CLASSIFICATION BASED ON STATE OF PROCESSES

Value Stream Mapping is broadly classified into two types, based on the state of processes.

They are,

• **Current State Value Stream Mapping,** also known as the Real State, or the AS-IS State, or the True State Value Stream Mapping.

• **Future State Value Stream Mapping,** also known as the Desired State, or the Ideal State Value Stream Mapping.

Current State Value Stream Mapping

Current State Value Stream Mapping , is also known as the Real State, or the AS-IS State, or the True State Value Stream Mapping.

This is the value stream mapping of the current or the AS-IS process.

This type of mapping usually maps the process as it is, in its truest form, with the wastes present.

It maps the process as it is in the current moment, without any bias or without any inclination towards the ideal state or hypothetical best state.

Future State Value Stream Mapping

Future State Value Stream Mapping , is also known as the Desired State, or the Ideal State Value Stream Mapping.

This is the value stream mapping of the future or the TO-BE process.

This type of mapping usually maps the process as it should be, in its best or ideal form, free of wastes.

It maps the process as it will be in the future, after all the wastes in the process are either eliminated or reduced.

The following figure depicts the different types of Value Stream Mapping, based on the state of the processes.

Value stream Mapping Types

Current State Value Stream Mapping

* Real State, AS-IS State, True State Value Stream Mapping.
* Current or the AS-IS process.
* Process as it is, in its truest form.
* With wastes present.

Future State Value Stream Mapping

* Desired State, Ideal State, Best State Value Stream Mapping.
* Future or the TO-BE process.
* Process as it should be, in its best or ideal form.
* With wastes eliminated or reduced.

BENEFITS OF VALUE STREAM MAPPING

Value Stream Mapping, is an integral and most important part of the lean tool kit.

Some of the key benefits of Value Stream Mapping are,

• It helps to map and present the current or the real process, as it is at the current moment.

• It helps to identify wastes in business processes.

• Its also helps in identifying the sources of wastes.

• It helps to present the value adding and non value adding activities in an easy to understand visual manner.

• It helps to understand the flow of information and time, in a logical way.

• It helps to map future or desired states of processes.

PARTS OF VALUE STREAM MAPPING

FLOWS IN THE VALUE STREAM MAP

There are three elements that flow in any Value Stream Map. They are, **Information**, **Process**, and **Time**.

Information is the data or the communication that flows in the Value Stream Map, and can flow bidirectionally, however it usually flows unidirectional from left to right, or from start to end of the process.

Process is the activities or steps of the process performed in sequence, in the Value Stream Map, and hence has to necessarily be unidirectional from left to right, or from start to end of the process.

Time is the time line of the activities or steps of the process in the Value Stream Map, and is again unidirectional from left to right, or from start to end of the process.

The following figure depicts the elements of the Value Stream Mapping, and the direction of their flows.

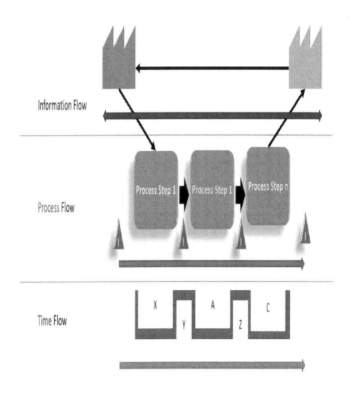

ICONS OF VALUE STREAM MAP

Value Stream Mapping makes use of shapes, symbols, and icons.

These icons are often times non standardized and can be customized as per need, and hence may vary from business to business or implementation to implementation.

However the icons representing a similar entities on different Value stream maps do appear similar and most times do resemble one another.

Depicted in the following figures are these icons in their general, non specific, common forms.

Process

An activity, or a step, or an operation of a process.

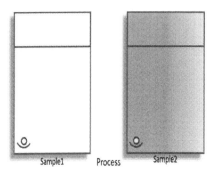

Production Control

A production scheduling or control department.

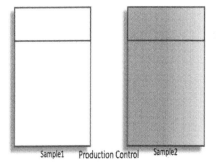

Schedule

A production or process schedule.

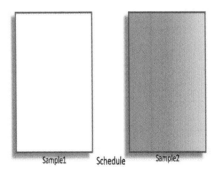

Sample1   Schedule   Sample2

Customer/Supplier

Supplier if present in the upper left corner, else a customer if present in the upper right corner.

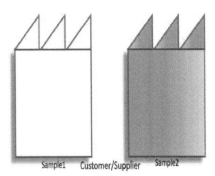

Sample1   Customer/Supplier   Sample2

Operator

An operator or the number of operators in the process.

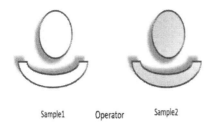

Sample1   Operator   Sample2

Go See

Visually check the process to gather information.

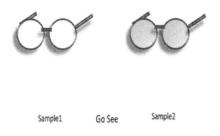

Sample1   Go See   Sample2

Shipment Arrow

Shipments of raw materials to factory or finished products to customers.

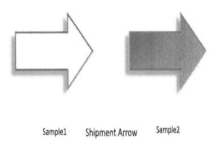

Sample1   Shipment Arrow   Sample2

Push Arrow

Pushing materials between steps, irrespective of a need.

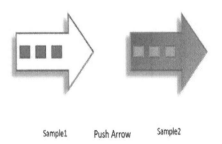

Sample1   Push Arrow   Sample2

Manual Information

Manual flow of information through mails, memo, reports etc.

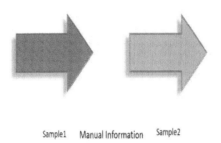

Sample1   Manual Information   Sample2

Electronic Information

Electronic flow of information through emails, EDI, fax etc.

Sample1   Electronic Information   Sample2

FIFO Lane

First In First Out inventory system to limit inputs.

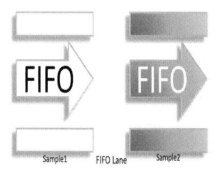

Sample1   FIFO Lane   Sample2

Load Leveling

A tool or system that levels Kanban batches to level production.

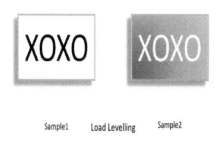

Sample1   Load Levelling   Sample2

U Cell

Multiple processes integrated into a single work cell.

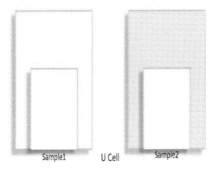

Kaizen Burst

Problem areas and improvement opportunities that need Kaizen workshops to reach ideal state.

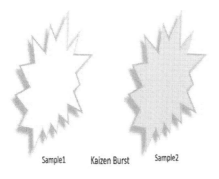

Production Kanban

Kanban card that signals the supplying process, to provide inputs to the next or downstream process.

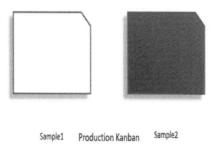

Sample1   Production Kanban   Sample2

Batch Kanban

Multiple Kanban cards sent or received in batches.

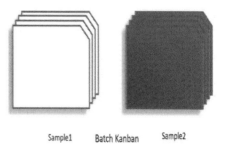

Sample1   Batch Kanban   Sample2

Withdrawal Kanban

Kanban card that signals to withdraw parts from a supermarket to a process.

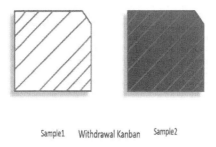

Sample1   Withdrawal Kanban   Sample2

Withdrawal Batch

Multiple Withdrawal Kanban cards in batches.

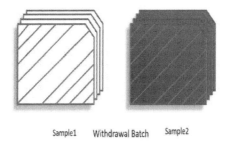

Sample1   Withdrawal Batch   Sample2

Supermarket

An inventory supermarket or Kanban stock point, where customers get stock, and is replenished by suppliers.

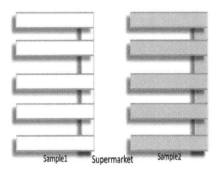

Sample1   Supermarket   Sample2

Buffer/Safety Stock

Temporary safety stock for emergency.

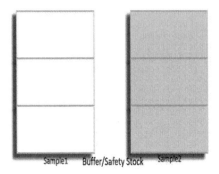

Sample1   Buffer/Safety Stock   Sample2

Signal Kanban

A Kanban signal to indicate when a supermarket inventory drops to minimum trigger point and needs supply.

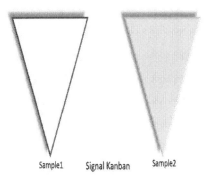

Sample1   Signal Kanban   Sample2

Inventory

A stored inventory or an inventory between two steps.

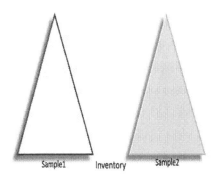

Sample1   Inventory   Sample2

Physical Pull

A physical removal of inventory from supermarket, to supply to further downstream processes.

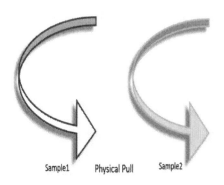

Sample1   Physical Pull   Sample2

Sequenced Pull

A sequenced pull of inventory from supermarket.

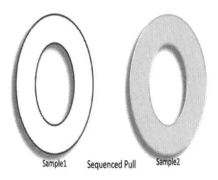

Sample1   Sequenced Pull   Sample2

Pull Arrow 1

Pulling of materials as per need.

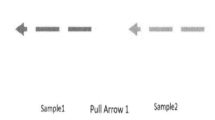

Sample1   Pull Arrow 1   Sample2

Pull Arrow 2

Pulling of materials as per need.

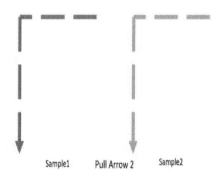

Sample1   Pull Arrow 2   Sample2

Pull Arrow 3

Pulling of materials as per need.

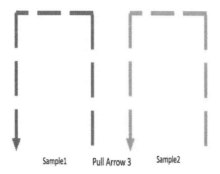

Pull Arrow 4

Pulling of materials as per need.

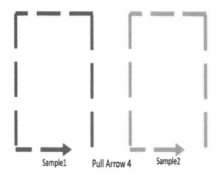

Kanban Post

Post or location to collect Kanban cards.

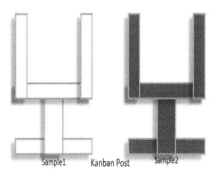

Sample1   Kanban Post   Sample2

Rail Shipment

Shipment of material transported in rail.

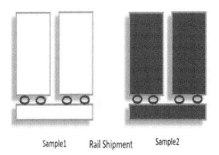

Sample1   Rail Shipment   Sample2

Road Shipment

Shipment of material transported on road.

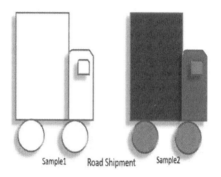

Sample1   Road Shipment   Sample2

Fork Lift Shipment

Shipment of material moved around on a fork lift.

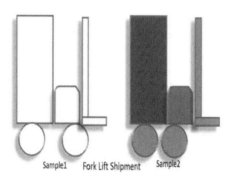

Sample1   Fork Lift Shipment   Sample2

Air Shipment

Shipment of material transported by air.

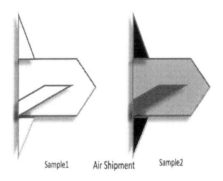

Sample1   Air Shipment   Sample2

Water Shipment

Shipment of material transported by water.

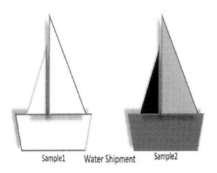

Sample1   Water Shipment   Sample2

Non Value Added Time

Waiting time in a process step.

Value Added Time

Process time in a process step.

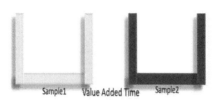

Timeline Total

Total value and non value added time in a process.

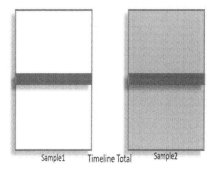

Data Table

Table or box to hold data.

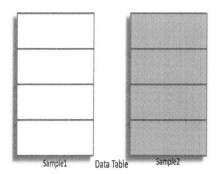

Data in Value stream mapping data table

The data tables can be used to display any of the below details, or more.

• Cycle Time.

• Change Over Time.

• Up Time or Net Available time.

• Production Rate or Takt Time..

• Scrap or Defect Rate.

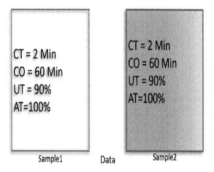

CT = 2 Min
CO = 60 Min
UT = 90%
AT=100%

Sample1   Data   Sample2

VALUE STREAM MAPPING PROCESS

VALUE STREAM MAPPING PROCESS

Often times Value Stream Mapping process consists of the following sequence of stages or steps, or its varieties.

Step 1 Prepare for Value Stream Mapping.

Step 2 Map Current State Value Stream.

Step 3 Perform Root Cause Analysis.

Step 4 Map Future State Value Stream.

Step 5 Implement Improvement.

Step 6 Standardize.

Prepare for Value Stream Mapping

Before proceeding with the Value Stream Mapping process, it is essential to first prepare well for it. The activities of this stage will include,

Selecting the process to improve or lean.

Obtaining management approval to start.

Selecting the Value Stream Mapping team.

Selecting the Value Stream Mapping Owner.

Providing necessary resources to ensure success.

Drawing the COPIS.

Map Current State Value Stream

Mapping the current state value stream stage should include following activities,

Perform Value Stream Mapping of the current process.

Identify Value Adding, Value Enabling, and Non Value Adding activities in the current process.

Identify the wastes in the current process.

Visually chart the distribution of the non value and value adding activities to understand total waste.

Perform Root Cause Analysis

Use this stage to identify the root causes behind the wastes by including the following activities,

Identify the root causes by asking Why, using the 5 Whys.

Additionally you can perform the following activities as well, if the solution is not direct and obvious.

Categorize the root causes using the Ishikawa diagram.

Identify the root causes to fix by using the Control Impact Matrix.

Map Future State Value Stream

Mapping the future state value stream stage should include following activities,

Perform Value Stream Mapping of the future process.

Visually chart the distribution of the non value and value adding activities to understand total waste reduction possible, to state the target improvements.

Implement Improvement

Implementing the improvement will often times include following activities,

Design Solution.

Develop Solution.

Test Solution.

Calculate improvements.

Standardize Solution

Once the solution is designed, developed, and tested, and improvements confirmed, the final stage will be to standardize the solution and will often times include following activities,

Present Improvements to management.

Educate and train the users on the new improved process.

Establish the future state value stream map as the present state.

The following figure depicts the Value Stream Mapping process.

.

CASE STUDY FOR VALUE STREAM MAPPING

To better understand the value stream mapping process, let's pick up a classic and most relevant case study of moving from functional layout to cellular layout in a burger shop.

For the sake of simplicity let's assume that the ingredients of the burger like the Bread, Cheese, Vegetables, Meat, and Salt and Pepper are considered similar to functions or departments and kept in separate areas.

And to make the burger the baker walks across these areas to pick up the ingredients one by one, makes the sub product in each area, and walks to the next area to create the next sub product till he completes creating the burger.

Often times in such scenarios or layouts, for increasing the effectiveness, and reducing costs, sub products are built in batches, which is an essence of mass production.

The below figure depicts this process for better understanding.

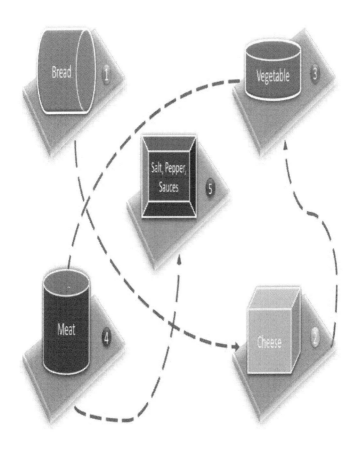

PREPARE FOR VALUE STREAM MAPPING

As we saw earlier preparing for the Value Stream Mapping is the first stage in the Value stream mapping process, and needs to be carried out with utmost attention for best results. The activities of this stage should include,

Selecting the process to improve or lean

For selecting the process to improve, you can look at the various product families in the business, connect to the people actually working in the Gemba, or connect with leadership and management to identify the process to improve. Often times, one can even pick up the processes in which one is working on a daily basis for the improvement. Another good place to look for improvement opportunities is the incident or service management tools where all the current and previous incidents and service requests are managed. Another place to check out is the SOP documentations of the processes. Also if the business maintains production process, and transaction process matrices, even those can be referred.

Obtaining management approval to start

Once you have selected a few processes which you feel can be improved, then you can look at those processes for the following,

• Which processes, if improved can deliver the maximum return on investment.

• Which processes, if improved can result in improving the most key performance indicators of your business.

• Which processes, do you think have most of the problems as reported by the customer?

• Which processes, do you think have most of the problems as reported by the people of your company?

• Which processes, do you think the management, the leadership, or the business cares for the most?

Once you have these points clear, you need to present your findings and proposal to improve the processes, to your management.

You can start your Value stream mapping exercise only if your business management give you a go ahead or a sign off to start the process.

Selecting the Value Stream Mapping team

For selecting the value stream mapping team, you may want to pick up people from the areas through which the value stream is flowing.

Team leaders, managers, operators and other workforce who are part of the value streams, and who perform related tasks daily are the best to pick from.

As, such people will have the necessary knowledge required to correctly map the process, identify the wastes, find out the root causes, and implement fixes.

Selecting the Value Stream Mapping Owner

Most Often businesses are arranged in terms of departments or functions.

Often times, the result of this is that there is no single person or entity to manage and own the value streams, instead there are departmental owners.

Hence to carry out the value stream mapping process to success, you might need a person to understand the value stream, identify the wastes, analyze the root causes, and implement fixes.

In short, you might need an end to end value stream mapping process owner.

Such a person should be empowered with visibility, and access to the business leaders, functions and departments.

And, be authorized to drive change and improvements across the various functional departments.

Avoid the tendency to split the value stream mapping process between the departments, as most often wastes are found within the hand offs that happen between the departments, rather than within departments.

Providing necessary resources to ensure success

Once the team, and an owner are identified, the next step you may want to do is to find out and provide the resources the value stream mapping team might need to successfully complete the exercise.

Planning and providing the required resources at this moment, helps reduce unnecessary delays later on.

One important task you may want to do at this time, is to introduce the identified value stream map team to the various departments, managers, leaders who might be the potential stakeholders of the process, to ensure their help and support can be obtained as needed during the exercise.

Draw the COPIS diagram

The next and the last step of the first stage is to provide a strong back bone to the value stream map, in the form of COPIS.

COPIS is a high level map or flow chart of the process which helps in identifying the process boundaries in terms of the following, **Customer, Output, Process, Input, and Supplier**

This enables the entire value stream mapping team to get a birds view of the process and a general idea before diving into in depth analysis.

The following figure depicts the COPIS for the chosen process.

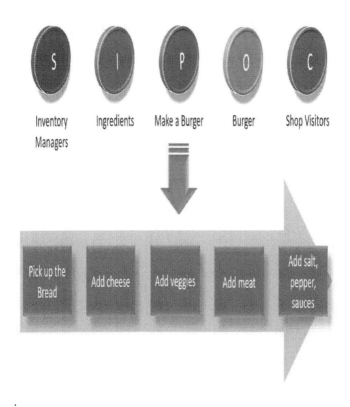

.

MAP CURRENT STATE VALUE STREAM

As we saw earlier mapping the current state value stream is the second stage in the Value stream mapping process, and should include following activities,

Perform Value Stream Mapping of the current process

This is where we actually map the current value stream. To make this process simple, follow the below steps one by one,

• Place the supplier and customer icons on the left and right top side of the page.

• Place the production control icons on the top center of the page.

• Place the process icons on the center of the page.

• Draw the Information, Process, and Time flows.

• Draw the various shipments and inventory icons.

• Place the details like cycle time, changeover time, up time, and availability of shared equipment as needed.

• Draw the time line total box.

• Place the Kaizen Bursts.

• Add any other details as per your need.

The following figure depicts the current state value stream mapping.

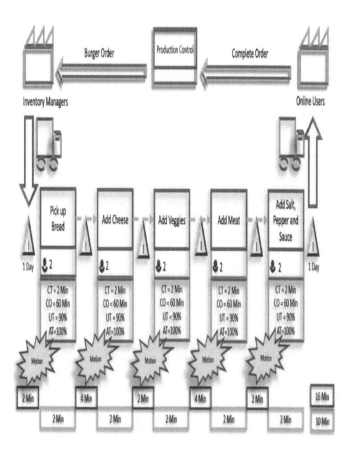

This diagram may appear too complex in the first glance, however, if you break down the parts and construct it, then mapping the value stream becomes much easier.

The following figures will help you understand this.

• Begin by placing the supplier and customer icons on the left and right top side of the page.

• Followed by placing the production control icon on the top center of the page.

• Then place the process icons on the center of the page.

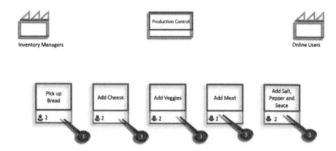

• Followed by drawing the Information, Process, and Time flows.

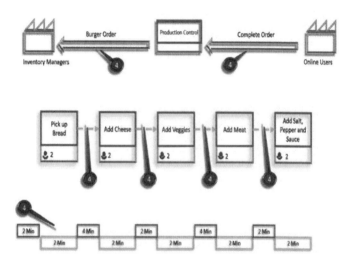

• Then draw the various shipments and inventory icons.

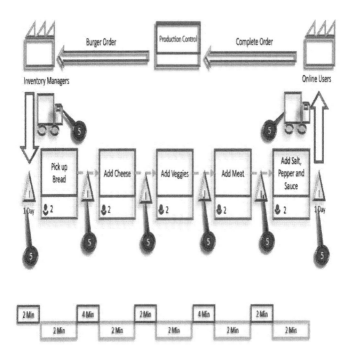

• Followed by placing the details like cycle time, changeover time, up time, and availability of shared equipment as needed.

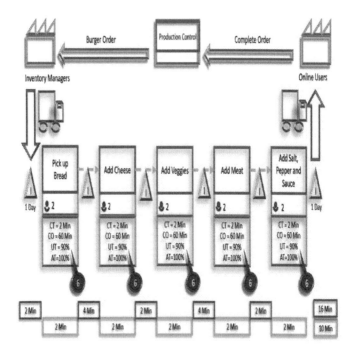

• Then draw the time line total boxes.

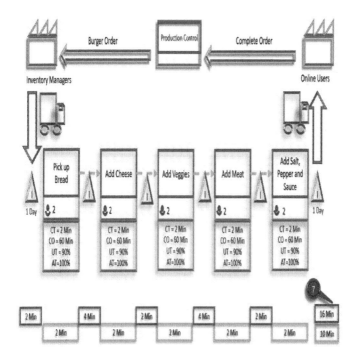

• And finally followed by placing the Kaizen Bursts.

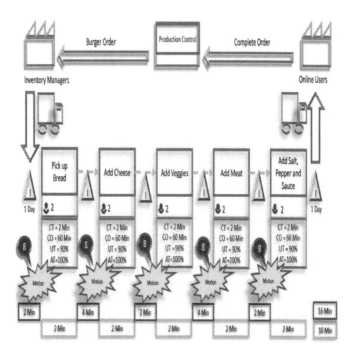

Identify Value Adding, Value Enabling, and Non Value Adding activities in the current process

From the Value Stream Map drawn for the current state, it is easy to identify the value adding, and the non value adding activities.

The more detailed the value stream map, the more easier to identify the non value added activities.

In the case study example we clearly see that all the process lead time is in fact the non value added activities.

Identify the wastes in the current process

To eliminate the wastes, in the process, and to make it lean you need to identify the wastes.

Again from the current value stream map we can see that the process in the case study has a high amount of motion waste, as the baker(s) have to walk around the various functions or department areas that hold the ingredients.

Visually chart the distribution of the non value and value adding activities to understand total waste

This is the last activity of the second stage, and is very important as it enables us to visualize the distribution of the wastes and the value adding activities.

Pie and bar charts are best for the purpose, as can be seen in the following figure which depicts a pie chart displaying the distribution of value adding and non value adding activities in the current process.

The current state value stream map reveals that there is around 61.5% of waste hidden in it.

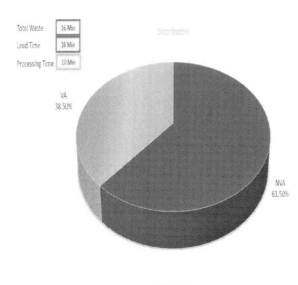

.

PERFORM ROOT CAUSE ANALYSIS

As we saw earlier identifying the root causes behind the wastes is the third stage in the Value stream mapping process, and should include following activities.

Identify the root causes by asking Why, using the 5 Whys

Asking 'Why' 5 times is probably the simplest and most straight forward technique to unravel the root causes behind any problem.

For the case we are studying, the problem would be "The burger making process is neither effective nor cost efficient".

So, the first Why in this case would be - "Why is the burger making process neither effective nor cost efficient?"

The answer for the first Why would be "Because there are wastes of motion in the process".

So, the second Why in this case can be - "Why are there wastes of motion in the process?"

The answer for the second Why would be "Because the baker(s) need to walk around a lot while making the burger".

The third Why would then probably be - "Why do the baker(s) need to walk around a lot while making the burger?"

The answer for the third Why would probably be "Because the baker(s) need to walk long distances to pick up ingredients used to make the burger".

The fourth Why proceeding further, would likely be - "Why do the baker(s) need to walk long distances to pick up ingredients used to make the burger?"

The answer for which would be "Because the ingredients are placed as per the type of the ingredient in different cupboards or areas, which act as inventory".

The fifth Why following the same pattern would then be - "Why are ingredients placed as per the type, and in different areas?"

The answer for which would be "Because the ingredients are placed as per a functional type of layout, where ingredients of same type are kept together".

By now we have reached the root cause for the problem which is - The ingredients are placed in what appears to be a functional layout, where similar type ingredients are placed together at a distance from one another.

The following figure depicts the 5 Whys root cause analysis in action.

Problem	The burger making process is neither effective nor cost efficient
1st Why	Why is the burger making process neither effective nor cost efficient?
2nd Why	Why are there wastes of motion in the process?
3rd Why	Why do the baker(s) need to walk around a lot while making the burger?
4th Why	Why do the baker(s) need to need to walk long distances to pick up ingredients used to make the burger?
5th Why	Why are ingredients placed as per the type, and in different areas?
Root Cause	The ingredients are placed in what appears to be a functional layout, where similar type ingredients are placed together at a distance from one another

MAP FUTURE STATE VALUE STREAM

As we saw earlier mapping the future state value stream is the fourth stage in the Value stream mapping process, and should include following activities,

Perform Value Stream Mapping of the future process

This is where we map the future value stream. Remember the future state value stream mapping is the hypothetical best state that we are trying to achieve as of now. To make this process simple, follow the below steps one by one, as performed for the current state value stream mapping.

• Place the supplier and customer icons on the left and right top side of the page.

• Place the production control icons on the top center of the page.

• Place the process icons on the center of the page.

• Draw the Information, Process, and Time flows.

• Draw the various shipments and inventory icons.

• Place the details like cycle time, changeover time, up time, and availability of shared equipment as needed.

• Draw the time line total box.

• Place the Kaizen Bursts.

• Add any other details as per your need.

The following figure depicts the future state value stream mapping.

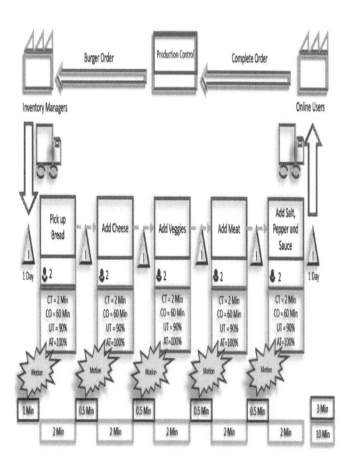

Visually chart the distribution of the non value and value adding activities to understand total waste reduction possible

This is the last activity of the fourth stage, and is very important as it enables us to visualize the possible reduction in the wastes, that can be achieved after the value stream mapping exercise.

Pie and bar charts are best for the purpose, as can be seen in the following figure which depicts a pie chart displaying the distribution of value adding and non value adding activities of the future state process.

The future state value stream map reveals that it is possible to reduce the wastes to around 23.08%.

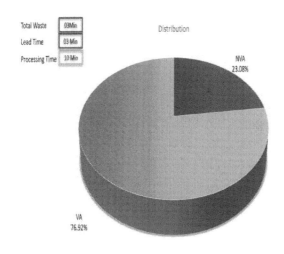

IMPLEMENT IMPROVEMENT

As we saw earlier implementing improvement in the value stream is the fifth stage in the Value stream mapping process, and should include following activities,

Design Solution

This is where we design the solution for creating the future value stream, by fixing the problem(s) that exist in the current value stream.

Remember, the root cause that we had found out behind the problems in the current state value stream mapping, was that - The ingredients are placed in what appears to be a functional layout, where similar type ingredients are placed together at a distance from one another .

So, to fix this issue or root cause, we need to move from a functional kind of a layout to a cellular **U Cell layout** layout which helps to implement what is known in the lean world as the famous **one piece flow**. Also, the ingredients need to be brought nearer to reduce the walking distance.

The solution, or the new layout should probably look something similar to the following depicted figure.

Develop Solution

This is the second activity of the fifth stage, and this is where the solution gets developed, or produced, or enhanced.

For the case that we are studying, this is where the new designed layout will actually be implemented.

Test Solution

Once the solution is designed and developed, it is imperative to check if it works well, as needed, and as expected.

So, in the third activity of the fifth stage. we ensure the correct working of the implemented solution by verifying and validating it.

Calculate improvements

This is the last activity of the fifth stage, and this is where the improvements are calculated.

A successful value stream mapping often results in drastic waste reductions, as we can see depicted in the below figure.

Metric	Before	After	Improvement
Total Waste	16 min	3 min	81.25%
Non Value Added Activity	61.50%	23.08%	38.42%
Value Added Activity	38.50%	76.92%	38.42%

.

STANDARDIZE SOLUTION

As we saw earlier standardizing the improvement is the sixth and the last stage in the Value stream mapping process, and should include following activities,

Present Improvements to management

This is where you can showcase the results of executing the value stream mapping exercise to the management to get a formal closure sign off.

You can include metrics like total waste reduction achieved, reduction in the non value added activity, and so on.

The following figure, depicts a way you can present the improvement achieved to the various departments and overall management and leadership.

Metric	Before	After	Improvement
Total Waste	16 min	3 min	81.25%
Non Value Added Activity	61.50%	23.08%	38.42%
Value Added Activity	38.50%	76.92%	38.42%

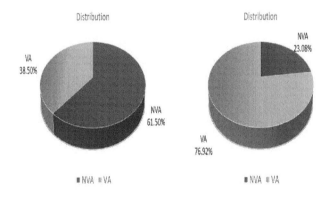

Educate and train the users on the new improved process

This is the second activity of the sixth stage, and is very important before base lining the new process.

This is where you educate the operators, and the workforce to use the new improved waste free process.

You can educate the workforce, the users, and the management by conducting trainings, creating user manuals, preparing FAQs, and so on.

Establish the future state value stream map as the present state

Once the solution is deployed, the future state value stream mapping which was developed earlier becomes the current state value stream map.

Value stream mapping then should be an ongoing activity, to keep up the kaizen spirit and the quest for achieving complete lean system by pursuing perfection.

The following figure depicts the future state value stream mapping which is now the current state value stream map.

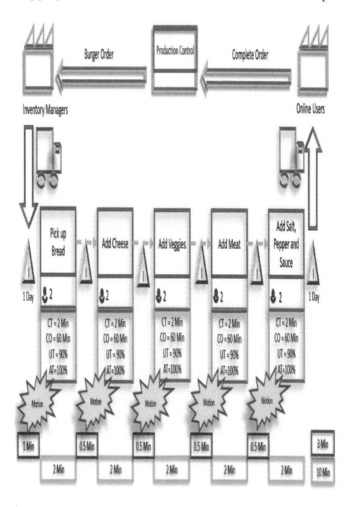

AUTHOR'S NOTE

I thank you for choosing the book, I have presented to you a detailed approach towards executing a value stream mapping exercise.

I hope this adds value to you and helps you eliminate wastes, and achieve cost reductions in your processes.

Please leave a review wherever you bought the book, and it will help me in my quest to provide good useful products to you on Lean Six Sigma.

All the very best,

Sumeet Savant
 Lean Six Sigma Master Black Belt and Coach

Printed in Great
Britain
by Amazon